Teen

C000218866

The ELI Readers collection is a
complete range of books and plays
for readers of all ages, ranging from
captivating contemporary stories
to timeless classics. There are three
series, each catering for a different
age group; Young ELI Readers, Teen
ELI Readers and Young Adult ELI
Readers. The books are carefully
edited and beautifully illustrated
to capture the essence of the
stories and plots. The readers are
supplemented with 'Focus on' texts
packed with background cultural
information about the writers and
their lives and times.

The TEMPEST
William Shakespeare

Retold and Activities by Silvana Sardi
Illustrated by Cristina Spanò

Teen ELI Readers

The Tempest
by William Shakespeare
Retold and Activities by Silvana Sardi
Language Level Consultant: Alison Smith
Illustrated by Cristina Spanò

ELI Readers
Founder and Series Editors
Paola Accattoli, Grazia Ancillani, Daniele Garbuglia (Art Director)

Graphic Design
Airone Comunicazione - Sergio Elisei

Layout
Airone Comunicazione

Production Manager
Francesco Capitano

Photo credits
Shutterstock

Typeset in 13 / 18 pt Monotype Dante

Printed in Italy by Tecnostampa Recanati - ERT240.01
ISBN 978-88-536-2019-4

First edition: March 2015

www.elireaders.com

Contents

These icons indicate the parts of the story that are recorded

start ▶ **stop** ■

PROSPERO

THE REAL DUKE
OF MILAN

ALONSO

KING OF NAPLES

MIRANDA

PROSPERO'S
DAUGHTER

CALIBAN

SON OF THE
WITCH SYCORAX

ANTONIO

PROSPERO'S BROTHER

GONZALO

A KIND MAN

ARIEL

SPIRIT

FERDINAND

ALONSO'S SON

STEPHANO

A SAILOR

SEBASTIAN

ALONSO'S BROTHER

Before you read

Grammar for KEY (KET)

**1 Read about Shakespeare. Choose the correct word
(A, B or C) to complete the text.**

William Shakespeare (**0**) ....*B*..... born in Stratford-upon-
Avon, (**1**) .... April 1564.
He was the eldest son and studied (**2**) .... at school.
When he (**3**) .... eighteen, he got married (**4**) ....
Anne Hathaway and they (**5**) .... three children. In
1584, he went (**6**) .... London and started working for
a theatre. He wasn't a really good actor, but the plays he
wrote became (**7**) .... popular. People went to see
(**8**) .... at the Globe Theatre. He wrote plays about
history, love and also sad stories. In (**9**) .... plays, you
can find stories about all different kinds of people and
they are often about families. At the end of his life, he
returned to Stratford, where he (**10**) .... at the age of
fifty-two.

0	**A** is	**B** was	**C** has been
1	**A** on	**B** in	**C** at
2	**A** many	**B** very	**C** hard
3	**A** was	**B** had	**C** has
4	**A** with	**B** to	**C** together
5	**A** had	**B** did	**C** have
6	**A** at	**B** to	**C** in
7	**A** much	**B** lots	**C** very
8	**A** it	**B** them	**C** their
9	**A** his	**B** your	**C** her
10	**A** dead	**B** died	**C** has died

Writing

2 Answer the following questions.

1 Would you like to go to the theatre? Why/why not?
2 Do you like going to the cinema? Why/ why not?
3 What kind of TV programmes do you like and why?

Vocabulary

3 Read and complete the missing word.

	You can read a story in this.	b<u>o</u> <u>o</u> <u>k</u>
1	Very bad weather.	s_ _ _ _
2	You can travel on this at sea.	s_ _ _
3	The queen is married to this man.	k_ _ _
4	Your father's brother for you.	u_ _ _ _
5	This has water all around it.	i_ _ _ _ _
6	A place with a lot of trees.	w_ _ _

Listening

▶3 **4 Listen to Act 1 Scene 2 and decide if these sentences are true (T) or false (F).**

		T	F
	The people on the ship aren't in any real danger.	☑	☐
1	Miranda's father was the King of Naples.	☐	☐
2	Miranda and her father now live on an island.	☐	☐
3	Miranda has got a brother called Antonio.	☐	☐
4	Ariel isn't free yet.	☐	☐
5	Caliban is good and kind.	☐	☐
6	Ferdinand doesn't want to leave Miranda.	☐	☐

Act 1

▶ 2 **Act 1 Scene 1**

On a ship at sea. It's stormy.

[Enter sailor*, Alonso, Sebastian, Antonio, Ferdinand and Gonzalo.]

ALONSO. Good sailor, be careful! Where's the captain*?

SAILOR. Please, go below.

ANTONIO. Where's the captain?

SAILOR. Can't you hear me? Go to your rooms! All of you!

GONZALO. Remember who you're talking to!

SAILOR. I love my king, but now we must work against the tempest*. Please, go back to your rooms. It's dangerous here!

GONZALO. I'm sure you can save us.

SAILOR. I'm afraid all is lost. The ship is going down.

SEBASTIAN. Swim for your life!

FERDINAND. Father!

ALONSO. My son!

[Exit all.]   ■

---

sailor a person who works on a ship   **captain** the head of the ship
tempest a storm

▶ 3 **Act 1 Scene 2**

An island. In front of Prospero's cave*.

[*Enter Prospero and Miranda. They look at the sea.*]

MIRANDA. Father, please stop this storm with your magic. Maybe somebody is in danger. Look! A ship is going down! Can you do nothing to help the people?

PROSPERO. Don't worry, my dear daughter. I've organised it all. Everybody on the ship will soon be safe. I've done all this for you, Miranda. You don't know anything about your past. You know only that I'm your father and that I live in a poor cave. You were only three when we came here. Can you remember anything before that?

MIRANDA. Certainly, father, I can.

PROSPERO. What? Please tell me, my child.

MIRANDA. For me, it's like a dream. Didn't I have four or five women who looked after me?

PROSPERO. Yes, you did, and more, Miranda. Twelve years ago, I, your father, was Duke of Milan. You were my only child and had everything you needed.

cave

MIRANDA. What happened to bring us to this island?

PROSPERO. Well, I wanted more time to study art, magic and other subjects, so I asked my brother Antonio to become Duke of Milan.

MIRANDA. You mean I've got an uncle?

PROSPERO. Yes, my dear child; but he wasn't a good man. After he became Duke, Antonio planned to kill us. Alonso, the King of Naples, helped him.

MIRANDA. So, how did we get to this island?

PROSPERO. Antonio took us on a ship far out at sea. Then, he pushed us into a smaller boat and left us there to die. Fortunately, a kind man, Gonzalo, put some food and water in the boat for us. He even remembered my book about magic! Many days later, we arrived on this island.

MIRANDA. Oh! My poor father! Was I a problem for you?

PROSPERO. Not at all; you were wonderful.

MIRANDA. Thank you, father, for all you've done for me; but why did you start the tempest?

PROSPERO. The King of Naples and my terrible brother Antonio are on that ship out there. The ship is going down, and they'll have to swim to this island. Then, I'll teach them a lesson. Now, sleep my child. [*aside.*] I must speak to the spirit*, Ariel.

[*With Prospero's magic, Miranda closes her eyes and sleeps.*]

PROSPERO. Ariel! My good spirit! Where are you?

[*Enter Ariel.*]

ARIEL. Here I am, great Prospero!

PROSPERO. Well, my good spirit, how did you do your business?

ARIEL. As you told me. There was a terrible storm and the angry sea washed over the ship!

PROSPERO. Was anybody afraid?

ARIEL. Yes, everybody! Ferdinand, the king's son, was the first to jump into the sea. Then, all the others followed.

PROSPERO. That's my spirit! But, were they near the island?

ARIEL. Yes, they're all safe on different parts of the island. Ferdinand is well, but he's sad because he thinks his father, the king, is lost at sea.

PROSPERO. Wonderful, Ariel! Bring him here; my daughter, Miranda, must meet this young

spirit a supernatural or magical being

prince*. What about the king and my brother?

ARIEL. They're looking for Ferdinand. The captain and the sailors are all on the island too. Even the ship is safe, but they don't know this.

PROSPERO. Ariel, you've done a good job; but there's still more work to do.

ARIEL. More work? But, am I not free now? I've done everything you asked.

PROSPERO. Ariel! Don't you remember when you were inside a tree and couldn't move?

ARIEL. Yes, the witch, Sycorax, put me there.

PROSPERO. Yes, she kept you there for twelve years. After Sycorax died, her terrible son, Caliban, became head of the island. You were still in the tree when I found you. Do you remember now?

ARIEL. Yes, great Prospero. And now, Caliban works for you! You've been so good to me, Prospero. Thank you! What can I still do for you?

PROSPERO. Bring me Ferdinand. I'll wake up Miranda so she can meet the prince.

ARIEL. Of course!

[*Exit Ariel.*]

PROSPERO. Wake up, Miranda, my sweet child!

prince the king's son

15

MIRANDA. Father, have I slept for a long time?

PROSPERO. Enough. Let's talk. Oh! We need wood for the fire. Where's that lazy Caliban?

MIRANDA. I don't know. I don't like him. He's never been kind to me.

PROSPERO. I know. He's almost worse than his mother, the witch, Sycorax. [*shouting.*] Caliban!

[*Enter Caliban.*]

CALIBAN. I'm coming!

PROSPERO. Get some wood for the fire! Can't you see there isn't any?

CALIBAN [*aside*]. I must do as he says because he can use his magic against me, but I hate him. He took this island from me!

PROSPERO. Caliban! Did you hear me?

CALIBAN. Yes! I'll get it now!

[*Exit Caliban.*]

PROSPERO. So, Miranda, now we can talk. Oh look! Somebody is coming this way.

[*Enter Ariel, followed by Ferdinand. Only Prospero can see Ariel, but Ferdinand can hear the spirit singing, and has followed the sound.*]

FERDINAND. Where's this music coming from?

While I was crying for my dear father, this song came across the water. I started to follow it, and now I feel less angry and sad.

PROSPERO. Miranda, what can you see? The only man you've ever seen is me, your father.

MIRANDA. Oh father! It's beautiful to see! What is it? Is it a spirit?

PROSPERO. No, my child; it eats and sleeps like us. This is a young man; he was on the ship that was in the tempest. He's handsome*, but he's sad because he has lost the people he was travelling with and is trying to find them.

MIRANDA. My father, I've never seen a man as handsome as this!

PROSPERO [aside]. Well done Ariel; everything is going as planned.

[Ferdinand sees Miranda, and thinks she's amazing.]

FERDINAND. You're so beautiful; you must be the queen of this magic island. Please, stay here with me and give me some good advice.

MIRANDA. I'm not a queen, just a girl.

FERDINAND: Oh how wonderful! The sweet girl speaks my language!

handsome beautiful

PROSPERO [*aside*]. It's love already! But first, I
　must be sure about Ferdinand [*to Ferdinand*].
　I'm afraid you want my island, young man!

MIRANDA [*aside*]. Why does my father speak so?

FERDINAND. Please, believe me, it's not true!

MIRANDA. Please father, he's a good young man.

PROSPERO [*to Ferdinand*]. Follow me! [*to Miranda*].
　Don't speak for him; he's come to steal from us
　[*to Ferdinand*]. Come! Leave my daughter alone!

FERDINAND. No! I want to stay here with her!

[*Ferdinand pulls out his sword*, but Prospero, with his
　magic, stops him.*]

MIRANDA. Please father, don't be too hard on him.

PROSPERO. Be quiet! Believe me, there are many
　more who are better than him.

MIRANDA. I don't want a better man.

PROSPERO [*to Ferdinand*]. Follow me to my cave!

FERDINAND. I can't stop myself; but I don't mind.
　I'll do anything to see this beautiful girl again.

MIRANDA. Don't be afraid, my father is good.

PROSPERO. My child, be quiet! Come, young man!

[*Exit all.*] ■

sword

Stop & Check

1 **Choose A, B or C to make true sentences about Act 1.**

On the ship, there was
A Miranda   **B** Alonso   C Prospero

1 When Miranda first came to the island she was
A 3 years old   **B** 4 years old   C 5 years old

2 Prospero and Miranda have been on the island for
A 3 years   **B** 12 years   C 10 years

3 Antonio is
A Miranda's   **B** Miranda's   C Miranda's
   brother   cousin   uncle

4 Prospero was helped by
A Alonso   **B** Gonzalo   C Antonio

5 Ariel was put in a tree by
A Prospero   **B** Sycorax   C Caliban

6 Ferdinand is
A a prince   **B** a spirit   C a king

Grammar

2 **Choose the correct word.**

Prospero hasn't seen some*body* / *anybody* from home for years.

1 *Everything* / *everybody* on the ship was afraid of the storm.

2 Caliban doesn't like *anybody* / *nobody* on the island.

3 Prospero organised *anything* / *everything* to bring his brother to the island.

4 Miranda remembers *something* / *anything* about her past.

5 Ferdinand will do *everything* / *everywhere* to see Miranda again.

6 Ferdinand doesn't know *anything* / *something* about Miranda.

Writing

3 You're Ferdinand. Write a page of your diary. Talk about:

- the storm   - the island   - Miranda

Pre-reading Activity

Listening KEY (KET)

▶ 4 **4 Listen to Act 2 Scene 1 and choose the correct answer – A, B or C.**

Alonso is looking for
A ☐ his brother.
B ☑ his son.
C ☐ his daughter.

1 Sebastian is surprised because
A ☐ their clothes aren't wet.
B ☐ their clothes have become old.
C ☐ their clothes are dirty.

2 Alonso's daughter, Claribel
A ☐ has lost her husband.
B ☐ has married the King of Tunis.
C ☐ has gone to Naples.

3 Antonio wants to kill
A ☐ Sebastian.
B ☐ Alonso.
C ☐ Claribel.

4 Gonzalo wakes up because Ariel
A ☐ pulls his ear.
B ☐ takes his sword.
C ☐ sings in his ear.

5 Antonio says he heard
A ☐ elephants.
B ☐ lions.
C ☐ dogs.

Act 2

▶ 4 **Act 2 Scene 1**

Another part of the island.

[*Enter Alonso, Sebastian, Antonio and Gonzalo.*]

GONZALO. We're safe and should be happy for this.

ALONSO. I'll only be happy when I find my son, Ferdinand.

SEBASTIAN. How strange! Our clothes are dry and new again, like when we wore them at Claribel's wedding*.

ALONSO. My dear daughter, Claribel! First I lose you to your new husband, the King of Tunis; now, on our way home, I've lost my son Ferdinand to the sea!

SEBASTIAN. You're paying for your mistake with Claribel, my dear brother. She's too young to live so far from Naples.

GONZALO. Please hush! The man is already sad enough.

ANTONIO [*to Sebastian*]. Old Gonzalo is always ready to speak well of our King of Naples, your brother, Alonso.

wedding when two people get married

[*Enter Ariel. Nobody can see him, but they can hear his music. Alonso and Gonzalo close their eyes and sleep.*]

ANTONIO. Sebastian, you should be the next King of Naples. Ferdinand is lost at sea.

SEBASTIAN. What about Claribel? She's my brother's daughter.

ANTONIO. She's now Queen of Tunis and lives too far from Naples. Look at me; I'm Duke of Milan and better at the job than my brother Prospero. We must kill your brother, Alonso, as I killed Prospero. Then, you'll be King of Naples.

SEBASTIAN. I like your plan; but when? How?

ANTONIO. Now! I'll kill Alonso and you kill Gonzalo while they're sleeping.

ARIEL [*aside*]. No, you won't!

[*They pull out their swords, but Ariel sings in Gonzalo's ear. Gonzalo wakes up and Alonso too.*]

GONZALO. What are you doing with your swords?

ANTONIO. We heard lions.

ALONSO. I was sleeping and I heard no lions. Now I want to look for my son again. Come all of you and help me.

[*Exit all.*]

► 5 **Act 2 Scene 2**

A wood on the island.

[Enter Caliban.]

CALIBAN. I'm tired. Prospero can wait for the wood for his fire. I need a rest.

[Enter Stephano, a sailor. He worked as a waiter on the ship. Enter also Ariel. Caliban and Stephano can't see the spirit.]

ARIEL *[aside]*. There's Caliban; but, who's this other man?

STEPHANO. Oh! What have we got here? A friend? Or should I be afraid?

CALIBAN. Leave me alone! There are already enough people I hate.

STEPHANO. Hey! I'm the same. My name's Stephano. I was a waiter on the ship. Everybody always told me to do this and do that, all day. I hated them all!

CALIBAN. I'm Caliban. For me it's worse. I have to do everything Prospero says, and he uses his magic against me.

STEPHANO. Magic? I like that!

CALIBAN. Prospero has a book of magic. He keeps

it in his cave. Every afternoon he has a rest. I've got an idea. We can kill him together. Then, you can have his book of magic and I'll show you all the wonderful things on this island.

STEPHANO. Ha-ha! A beautiful island and a book of magic! Of course I'll help you, my sad little friend. Let's go!

ARIEL [*aside*]. I must tell Prospero of their plans.
[*Exit Ariel.*]

CALIBAN. Yes! Follow me Stephano. I'll take you to Prospero's cave. He keeps his book of magic there.

[*Exit all.*]　　　　　　　　　　　　　　⬛

Stop & Check

1 Complete the crossword about Act 2.

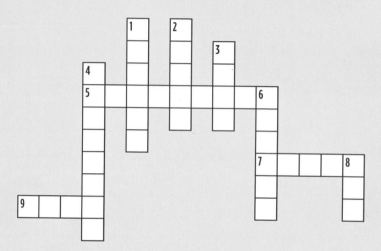

Across

5 Prospero has a rest at this time every day.

7 Antonio says he heard these.

9 Prospero keeps his book here.

Down

1 Stephano was this on the ship.

2 Antonio wants to use this to kill Alonso.

3 Caliban must bring this to Prospero.

4 Claribel is Alonso's ...

6 Sebastian wants to become King of ...

8 Alonso is looking for his ...

Vocabulary

2 Find the odd one out in each line.

	A island	**B** lake	**C** sea	**D** river
1	**A** husband	**B** son	**C** father	**D** aunt
2	**A** happy	**B** sad	**C** tired	**D** angry
3	**A** eye	**B** arm	**C** nose	**D** ear
4	**A** lion	**B** monkey	**C** cow	**D** elephant
5	**A** love	**B** hate	**C** prefer	**D** like
6	**A** school	**B** waiter	**C** artist	**D** chef
7	**A** storm	**B** ice	**C** snow	**D** sun

Writing for KEY (KET)

3 You're Caliban. Write to Stephano about your plan to kill Prospero. Tell him:

- where to meet   - what to bring   - what time to meet

Write 25-35 words.

Pre-reading Activity

Speaking

4 At the end of Act 2, Sebastian and Antonio are planning to kill Alonso and Gonzalo while Caliban and Stephano want to kill Prospero. What will happen in Act 3? Discuss these questions with a partner.

1 When will Antonio and Sebastian try to kill Alonso and Gonzalo?
2 What will Antonio and Sebastian use to kill them?
3 When will Caliban and Stephano kill Prospero?
4 Where will they kill him?

Act 3

▶ 6 **Act 3 Scene 1**

In front of Prospero's cave.

[Enter Ferdinand, carrying a heavy piece of wood.]

FERDINAND. This work is hard and I hate it, but at least I can see that sweet girl again. She's ten times nicer than her father. Prospero has told me to bring all this wood here.

[Enter Miranda, followed by Prospero. Prospero stands behind a tree. Miranda and Ferdinand can't see him. He listens to them talking.]

MIRANDA. Please, don't work so hard! Sit down and have a rest. My father is busy studying and won't know.

[Ferdinand sits down next to Miranda.]

FERDINAND. I should finish before night falls.

MIRANDA. I'll help you; give me some wood to carry.

FERDINAND. No, my sweet lady*; you mustn't do work like this. But, tell me, what's your name?

MIRANDA. Miranda – Oh! I forgot; my father told me to say nothing.

lady woman

[*Prospero laughs at his daughter's words, but they don't hear him.*]

FERDINAND. Oh Miranda! I've seen many beautiful women in my life, but you are perfect!

MIRANDA. I don't know any other women; only my own face in the mirror. As for men, I've only ever seen you and my father. I don't know any other men, but I know I only want you. Oops! I'm speaking too much and forgetting my father's advice.

FERDINAND. I'm a prince, Miranda. My name's Ferdinand. I'm afraid my poor father is lost at sea. I'm probably now King of Naples and you'll be my queen!

MIRANDA. Do you love me?

FERDINAND. Of course! I love you more than anything else in the world!

MIRANDA. I'm so happy, I could cry!

PROSPERO [*aside*]. Sweet love!

MIRANDA. Let's get married and I'll be your wife!

FERDINAND. Yes, my love!

MIRANDA. And you'll be my husband then?

FERDINAND. Yes, of course!

[*Prospero comes out from behind the tree.*]

PROSPERO. Ferdinand, I've heard everything. You've worked enough. I'm happy to give you my daughter's hand.

MIRANDA. Oh father!

PROSPERO. Don't worry, my child. I've heard your words of love and am happy for you both. Ferdinand, I only wanted to see if your love for my beautiful, sweet daughter was true.

FERDINAND. It is.

PROSPERO. Then go and talk some more. I have other business to do. I need my book.

MIRANDA. Thank you, my father! [*to Ferdinand.*] Come, my love, and tell me of your life.

[*Exit Miranda and Ferdinand, hand in hand.*]

PROSPERO. I must go and look for Ariel.

[*Exit Prospero.*] ■

▶1 **Act 3 Scene 2**

Another part of the island.

[Enter Alonso, Sebastian, Antonio and Gonzalo.]

GONZALO. My king, I can walk no more; I need to sit down.

ALONSO. My old friend, I too am tired. I'm afraid we'll never find my son, Ferdinand.

ANTONIO *[aside to Sebastian]*. Tonight, while they're sleeping, we'll kill them. Soon, you'll be King of Naples, Sebastian.

SEBASTIAN. *[aside to Antonio.]* Yes, with your help, my friend.

[Enter Ariel, singing. He's dressed as a waiter. He brings a table full of food and drink.]

[Exit Ariel.]

ANTONIO. Who brings us all this?

SEBASTIAN. Wonderful, sweet music! And look at all this food! Won't you try some?

ALONSO. Not I; I'm too sad to eat.

GONZALO. Please, try and eat something my dear king.

[Enter Ariel again. Now he's a horrible, big bird.]

ARIEL. Antonio! Alonso! You've been very cruel*
in your lives. Remember what you did to poor
Prospero. You'll go crazy with this thought.

ANTONIO. We're not afraid of you, strange bird.
We've got our swords! [*taking out sword.*]

ARIEL. Put away your sword; you can do nothing
with it against me. I'm too strong for you all.
Antonio, do you remember how you became
Duke of Milan? You put Prospero and his child
in danger in the open sea. That same sea has
become angry with you and has thrown you
onto this island.

ANTONIO. How can this bird know all this? Am I
going crazy?

ARIEL. I know all about you. Alonso, you've lost
your son. You and your friends are now
paying for all the bad things you've done.

[*Ariel leaves taking the food and drink with him.*]

GONZALO. What was that?

ALONSO. Oh it certainly wasn't a normal bird.
I thought I heard it shout Prospero's name.
Now I remember how horrible I've been. Poor
Prospero! His poor sweet daughter, lost at sea

cruel not kind

The Tempest

because of us, Antonio. I must find my son. I feel crazy.

[*Exit Alonso.*]

ANTONIO. Sebastian, let's go and look for this strange bird. Maybe it can tell us what happened to my poor brother and Ferdinand. I feel so sorry for what I did to Prospero. My head is full of strange thoughts.

SEBASTIAN. There's some strange magic on this island which has taken our thoughts. I'm also full of pity* for poor Prospero and his sweet child, Miranda, and I had nothing to do with the plan!

[*Exit Antonio and Sebastian.*]

GONZALO. They're all crazy. I must follow them and try to help them. Oh Prospero, are you still alive? I hope so!

[*Exit Gonzalo.*]

pity to feel sad and sorry for someone

Stop & Check

1 Answer the following questions about Act 3.

1 What does Ferdinand have to do for Prospero?
2 How many men has Miranda seen in her life?
3 What do Ferdinand and Miranda want to do?
4 What does Ariel first bring to Alonso and his friends?
5 What animal does Ariel become?
6 How does Alonso feel after listening to Ariel?

Vocabulary

2 Complete the sentences with a word from the box.

life	hand	rest	words	~~tree~~	mirror	help

Prospero hides behind a ...*tree*... to listen to Ferdinand and Miranda.

1 Miranda doesn't know any other women, only her own face in the ....
2 Ferdinand couldn't have a .... because he had a lot of work to finish.
3 Prospero is happy to give Ferdinand his daughter's ....
4 With Antonio's .... Sebastian plans to kill Alonso and Gonzalo.
5 Prospero laughs at his daughter's ....
6 In all his .... Ferdinand has never seen a woman as beautiful as Miranda.

Grammar for KEY (KET)

3 **Choose the best word (A, B or C) for each space.**

Ferdinand found the work ...*hard*... .

A hard   **B** much   **C** busy

1 Ferdinand .... to stay and talk to Miranda.

     A went   **B** decided   **C** finished

2 Prospero wanted to .... to them.

     A hear   **B** say   **C** listen

3 Ferdinand .... to finish before night fell.

     A should   **B** must   **C** had

4 Miranda .... her father's advice.

     A forgot   **B** gave   **C** did

5 Alonso was .... for his son.

     A trying   **B** watching   **C** looking

6 Miranda wants to get married .... Ferdinand.

     A with   **B** to   **C** at

Pre-reading Activity

Listening KEY (KET)

▶ 8, 9   **4** **Listen to Act 4 and decide if the following sentences are true (T) or false (F).**

	T	F
Ariel feels sorry for Alonso and Antonio.	☑	☐
1 Prospero sees Alonso and Antonio with his own eyes.	☐	☐
2 Caliban and Stephano want Prospero's book of magic.	☐	☐
3 Prospero wants to change his clothes before Caliban arrives.	☐	☐
4 Prospero wants to help Caliban and Stephano with his magic.	☐	☐
5 Caliban tries on the clothes with Stephano.	☐	☐
6 Some dogs run after Caliban and Stephano.	☐	☐

Act 4

▶ 8 **Act 4 Scene 1**

In front of Prospero's cave.

[Enter Prospero and Ariel.]

PROSPERO. At last, we've got time to talk, Ariel. Tell me everything.

ARIEL. Alonso and Antonio are crazy with the thought of what they did to you and Miranda.

PROSPERO. Are they really sorry?

ARIEL. Yes, I'm sure of this. I saw it with my own eyes and felt pity for them.

PROSPERO. If you who are a spirit can feel pity, then I, a man, will feel the same. Bring them to me. I'm ready to forgive* them now.

ARIEL. Yes, but I must also tell you that Antonio and Sebastian were planning to kill Alonso.

PROSPERO. What? My brother never learns.

ARIEL. Well, that was before they heard me and felt sorry, ha-ha!

PROSPERO. Ariel, thank you for all your help. I'll miss you when you go. Right, bring them here so I can speak to them!

forgive not be angry any more

ARIEL. I'll get them, kind Prospero; but there's just one more problem.

PROSPERO. What? Another problem?

ARIEL. I'm afraid it's Caliban again.

PROSPERO. Oh no! What has he done this time?

ARIEL. Caliban has met a waiter called Stephano. They're planning to come here and kill you. They want your book of magic.

PROSPERO. Humph! Caliban becomes worse every day. When do they plan to come?

ARIEL. They'll be here soon.

PROSPERO. Well, we must prepare for them. First, Ariel, put some beautiful clothes outside my cave.

ARIEL. I'll do it now.

PROSPERO. I'll look at my book to find the right piece of magic to stop them.

[*Exit all.*]

⏵9 **Act 4 Scene 2**

In front of Prospero's cave. Ariel has put beautiful clothes around the entrance to the cave. There are all different colours of coats, hats, jackets and trousers.

[*Enter Caliban, Stephano, Prospero and Ariel. Caliban and Stephano can't see Prospero and Ariel. Prospero and Ariel stand at the side and watch the other two.*]

CALIBAN. Here's Prospero's cave, Stephano. Go in and kill him. Then I'll be free and you can have his book of magic.

STEPHANO. Wait a minute, my friend. Look at all these beautiful clothes. I've never worn clothes like these! I must try them on.

[*Stephano puts on a beautiful coat and dances around.*]

STEPHANO. Ha-ha! Look at me, I'm king of the island.

CALIBAN. Shh, you'll wake up Prospero. I'm sure he's sleeping inside. Do the job first, then you can play.

STEPHANO. Hey Caliban! I'm not your waiter, you know. I want to have some fun first. Why don't you try something on too?

CALIBAN. You don't know Prospero.

STEPHANO. I'm afraid he'll hear us. Then, he'll use his magic against us.

[*Prospero aside to Ariel.*] He's right to be afraid. Now it's time for us to have some fun!

[*Prospero lifts both his arms. By magic, lots of dogs come running out from behind the trees.*]

STEPHANO. Hey! What's happening? Where have all these dogs come from?

CALIBAN. Oh no! I told you to stop playing with those clothes. Now look what has happened!

STEPHANO. What are you talking about?

CALIBAN. This is Prospero's magic!

STEPHANO. All I know, is I don't like those dogs' teeth. I don't want to be their next dinner. I'm going.

CALIBAN. Wait for me, Stephano!

[*Exit Stephano and Caliban running with the dogs behind them.*]

ARIEL. Ha-ha, Prospero! Your magic is always good, but this time it was brilliant!

PROSPERO. Thank you, dear Ariel. It was lucky that you told me about their plan.

ARIEL. Yes, it was lucky that I heard them talking about it!

PROSPERO. They can run around the island a few times with the dogs at their backs. Then, maybe, they'll be too tired to think about killing me!

ARIEL. I hope so! But, Prospero, what will you do with these two in the end?

PROSPERO. I don't know. I think I'll leave them on this island. I don't need it any more. They can try and live a good life without hurting anybody.

ARIEL. But without your magic, Prospero!

PROSPERO. Of course! They're too dangerous to have a book of magic!

ARIEL. Yes, you're right. The book of magic is only good in your hands.

PROSPERO. Thank you, Ariel.

PROSPERO. Now, bring me my brother and his friends, Ariel. It's time for us to meet. It's time to forgive and forget. It's time for you to be free too, Ariel.

ARIEL. I'll go now, dear kind Prospero.

[*Exit all.*]

Stop & Check

1 Put the sentences in the right order as they happen in Act 4.

A ☐ Ariel puts some clothes outside Prospero's cave.
B ☐ Stephano tries on a beautiful coat.
C ☑ Ariel tells Prospero that Alonso and Antonio are sorry.
D ☐ Prospero looks at his book of magic.
E ☐ Caliban tells Stephano to stop playing.
F ☐ Some dogs come out from behind the trees.
G ☐ Ariel tells Prospero about Stephano and Caliban.

Grammar

2 Choose the best word from the box to complete the sentences.

~~for~~	to	at	on	up	for	around

Ariel feels pity ....*for*.... Alonso and Antonio.

1 After running .... the island, Stephano and Caliban will be tired.
2 Caliban is planning .... kill Prospero.
3 Stephano tries .... a coat.
4 Caliban is afraid Prospero will wake ....
5 Stephano starts to run and doesn't wait .... Caliban.
6 Prospero looks .... his book of magic.

Speaking / Writing

3 Work in pairs. You're Prospero and Ariel. Talk about what you saw when Caliban and Stephano came to the cave. Then, write your conversation. Start like this:

ARIEL. Did you see Stephano's face when he saw the clothes?

PROSPERO. Yes, he really liked them. Did he put on the hat? I can't remember.

ARIEL. ....

PROSPERO. ....

ARIEL. ....

PROSPERO. ....

ARIEL. ....

PROSPERO. ....

ARIEL. ....

Pre-reading Activity

Listening

▶ 10 4 Listen to Act 5 and match the sentences to the person who says them.

I'll tell the wind to help you have
a safe journey.   Miranda
                                                   Prospero
1 I thought you were dead!   → Ariel
2 How does he know all these things?   Gonzalo
3 I'm just happy to have my brother again.   Alonso
4 Another handsome man!   Ferdinand
5 Who's this beautiful girl?   Sebastian
6 I've chosen her to be my wife.   Antonio
7 I'm the happiest man in the world.

Act 5

Act 5 Scene 1

Outside Prospero's cave. Entrance to cave covered by a curtain.

[Enter Prospero. He draws a circle in front of the cave.]

PROSPERO. I can hear Ariel. He's coming with my brother and the others. They'll stand in this magic circle until I'm sure that they're sorry for all they've done.

[Enter Ariel, followed by Alonso, Antonio, Sebastian and Gonzalo. Ariel brings them into the circle They stand there, while Prospero looks at them. They're afraid and don't understand who Prospero is.]

PROSPERO. I must speak to these men, but first, Ariel, you're free. You've done a wonderful job. I'll miss you.

ARIEL. Thank you, dear Prospero.

PROSPERO. One last thing; in the harbour*, you'll find the ship. The captain and all the sailors are sleeping. Go and wake them up and tell them to prepare the ship to go home.

harbour a place where ships stop after a journey

PROSPERO. Thank you, my dear friend; I'll never forget you.

[*Exit Ariel.*]

PROSPERO. Now, I must help these men. With my magic, they'll be free from their crazy thoughts.

[*Prospero moves his hands in the air. The circle breaks and the men aren't afraid any more. They still don't understand that they're looking at Prospero.*]

PROSPERO. First you, good Gonzalo! Thanks to you, all those years ago, my daughter and I arrived on this island after our terrible boat journey.

GONZALO. I'm sorry, but I don't understand. I don't know who you are.

PROSPERO. Gonzalo, I'm Prospero, the real Duke of Milan. You were so kind to me; do you remember now?

GONZALO. Of course! I thought you were dead! Instead, here you are in front of me! Oh, I'm so happy to see you again!

PROSPERO. Welcome also to Alonso, King of

Naples. You too were part of my brother Antonio's terrible plan, but I forgive you.

ALONSO. Are you really Prospero? I'm not sure. All I know is that I don't feel crazy anymore.

PROSPERO. Yes, it's me. And, Antonio! Should I call you my brother? You tried to kill me; but Ariel has told me that you're sorry for what happened so I forgive you too. I'll return to my country and be Duke of Milan again [*aside to Antonio and Sebastian*]. Don't worry, I won't tell Alonso you were planning to kill him.

SEBASTIAN [*aside to Antonio*]. How does he know all these things?

ANTONIO [*aside to Sebastian*]. I don't know. I'm just happy to have my brother again.

SEBASTIAN [*aside to Antonio*]. I'm happy for you too.

ALONSO. But, please tell us; how did you find us? We were looking for my lost son all over the island.

PROSPERO. I'm sorry that you've lost your son, Alonso. I too have lost a child, a daughter.

ALONSO. You? Your daughter? When?

PROSPERO. In the tempest. Anyway, you can be sure that I'm really Prospero, Duke of Milan. I've lived here for all these years in this cave. Alonso, please, look and see what's inside.

[*Prospero opens the curtain at the entrance to the cave. Alonso sees Ferdinand and Miranda. They're sitting playing chess.*]

ALONSO. If this is the magic of this island, then I've lost my son again!

FERDINAND: Father! The sea's been kind to you; you're safe!

MIRANDA. Another handsome man!

ALONSO. Who's this beautiful girl, Ferdinand?

FERDINAND. She's Prospero's daughter, Miranda. I've chosen her to be my wife.

ALONSO. Then, I must ask my future daughter to forgive me.

PROSPERO. No, Alonso. Everything is forgiven. Even you, Antonio, can feel happy; Miranda has met Ferdinand and will one day become Queen of Naples!

ANTONIO. Oh, my dear brother! Thank you for your kind words.

GONZALO. How wonderful! Ferdinand has found a wife and Alonso has found his son.

ALONSO. But how can we return home?

PROSPERO. Your ship and all your sailors are safe in the harbour.

ALONSO. More magic!

PROSPERO. Tonight, we'll eat together and I'll tell you the whole story. Then, in the morning, we'll leave for Naples, where our two dear children will be married. Then, to Milan, where I'll live the rest of my days.

[*Exit all except Prospero.*]

[*Prospero takes his book of magic and throws it into the sea.*]

PROSPERO. My sweet daughter has found love and will become Queen of Naples. I'll be Duke of Milan once more. No more magic; no more spirits; I don't need them anymore. I'm the happiest man in the world.

[*Exit Prospero.*]

Stop & Check

1 **Decide if the following sentences about Act 5 are true (T) or false (F).**

	T	F
Prospero waits for Ariel and the others in front of his cave.	☑	☐
1 Prospero will miss Ariel.	☑	☐
2 The captain and the sailors are on the ship.	☐	☑
3 Prospero is still angry with his brother.	☐	☑
4 Prospero says he lost his daughter in the storm.	☑	☐
5 Ferdinand and Miranda are playing cards in the cave.	☐	☑
6 One day, Miranda will become Queen of Milan.	☑	☐

Vocabulary

2 **Unscramble these verbs from Act 5**

WDRA — *DRAW*

1 LETL — T _ _ _
2 HOSECO — C _ _ _ _ _
3 NFDI — F _ _ _
4 RNGBI — B _ _ _ _
5 GTFROE — F _ _ _ _ _
6 TADSNDRNUE — U _ _ _ _ _ _ _ _ _

Grammar

3 Complete the sentences with the Past Simple of the verbs in exercise 2.

Prospero ..*drew*.. a circle in front of his cave.

1 Gonzalo finally .... who Prospero was.

2 Ariel .... Alonso and his friends to Prospero.

3 Alonso .... his son in Prospero's cave.

4 Prospero .... all the bad things about his brother's past.

5 Ferdinand .... Miranda to be his wife.

6 Prospero .... Alonso that his ship was in the harbour.

Speaking / Writing

4 Discuss the following questions in pairs, then write your answers.

1 Did you like *The Tempest*? Why / Why not?

....

....

....

2 Who did you like best in the play? Why?

....

....

....

3 Which part of the play did you like best? Why?

....

....

....

William Shakespeare
(1564 - 1616)

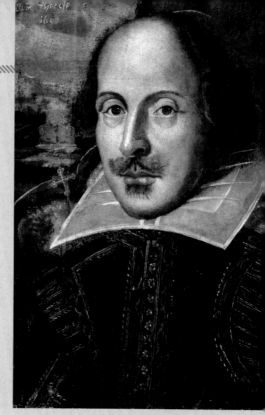

Stratford-upon-Avon

William Shakespeare was born in Stratford-upon-Avon. This is a town on the River Avon in south Warwickshire, England. It's home to the Royal Shakespeare Company, one of the most important theatre companies in Britain. Millions of tourists from all over the world come to Stratford-upon-Avon every year. They can visit the house where Shakespeare died, his daughter's home, and his wife's home before they got married.

Early life

Shakespeare's father, John, was a businessman who bought and sold wool and leather. His mother, Mary Arden, came from a rich family with a big farm. They had eight children, but three died when they were very young. William went to a school near his home, where he studied Latin writers. He soon began to love reading. In 1582, he married Anne Hathaway, a girl from a small village near his home. She was 26 and was eight years older than him. Their first child was a girl, Susanna, born in 1583. Then, they had twins, a boy, Hamnet, and a girl, Judith. Unfortunately, their son died when he was 11 years old.

London and Work

Shakespeare began working in London as an actor. Then, he started writing plays and, with some others, had a company of actors called *The Lord Chamberlain's Men*. He was not only a playwright* and is also known as *England's national poet*. He wrote most of his plays between 1589 and 1613. His first plays were almost always comedies, like *A Midsummer Night's Dream*. Plays like this one have a happy end. They are usually about people who love each other and want to get married. But there are many problems and it's funny to see how they are able to do it in the end. Next, Shakespeare started writing history plays, especially about English history, such as *Richard III*. Richard III was King of England at the end of the Middle Ages for just two years before he died in the War of the Roses. Shakespeare also wrote sad stories like *Romeo and Juliet*. Here, the two young people love each other, but they die at the end of the play. He wrote most of these sad plays, known as *Tragedies*, between 1601 and 1608 and some of the most famous ones of this time are *Macbeth* and *Hamlet*. Shakespeare's popularity grew over the years and people loved going to the theatre to watch his plays. However, in 1613, at the age of 49, he decided to leave London and go back to his home town, where he died 3 years later.

Task

Complete the information about Shakespeare.

First name:		*William*
Home town:	1	
Born (year):	2	
Nationality:	3	
Wife's name:	4	
Job:	5	
Name of theatre group:	6	
Died (year):	7	
Comedy:	8	
English history play:	9	
Tragedies:	10	

playwright a person who writes plays

The Elizabethan Theatre

Drama*

Drama was very popular during the Elizabethan age. Both Queen Elizabeth I and the ordinary people of that time enjoyed going to the theatre. English theatre was in many ways like Greek theatre. Each play had five acts and often told sad stories. However, some stories also came from Italian companies which acted in England in the 16th century. In these plays they spoke about love, horror, and people killing each other.

Theatres

At first, they performed* plays in the streets. Then, in 1567, they built the first English theatre in London, and called it *The Red Lion*. However, a lot of actors started to leave the capital because they were afraid of getting ill. So Elizabeth I ordered her people to build public* theatres, known also as *playhouses*, outside London. When the people in London were healthy again, the actors returned to the capital. *The Globe Theatre*, where they performed most of Shakespeare's plays, was built in London in 1599. All the theatres were different in some way, but they followed a general plan. They built them in a circle with the stage in the centre. These large, open-air public theatres didn't have a roof, and the people could sit around three sides of the stage. These buildings were made of wood, so they easily went on fire. This happened to the *Globe Theatre* in 1613, so they had to build it all again. The stage in these public theatres didn't have a curtain and there wasn't much on stage. The actors performed the plays during the day and everybody could come and watch them.

drama a story acted on stage
perform (-ed) to act, do

public for everybody

Playwrights and Drama Companies

All playwrights in the Elizabethan age were men. Shakespeare was both an actor and playwright but there weren't many like him. Acting companies paid playwrights to write a play. If it was performed, the playwright received the money from the first show. From then on, the play belonged to the theatre company and the playwright made no more money from it. Most playwrights wrote two plays a year. Shakespeare wrote about forty plays over twenty years. However, he was different from other playwrights because he also made money as an actor. Also, part of the theatre where his plays were performed, belonged to him. His drama company, *The Lord Chamberlain's Men*, was one of the most famous companies of that time. These drama companies included only men, so all parts for women were played by young boys in women's clothes. The actors worked six days a week and performed a different play every day. Costumes were expensive, so actors often wore their normal clothes on stage. Each company performed between thirty and forty new plays a year.

Task - Internet

Look on the internet and try and find the answer to these questions about the Elizabethan theatre.

- What time did the plays start and finish?
- How much did it cost to see a play?
- What plays were most popular?
- Other than Shakespeare, who else was a famous playwright at this time?

Choose A, B or C to complete the sentences.

At the start of the play, Ferdinand is on the ship with his

A sister   **B** father   **C** wife

1 Caliban is afraid of

A Ariel   **B** Miranda   **C** Prospero

2 Stephano becomes friends with

A Caliban   **B** Ferdinand   **C** Antonio

3 Prospero keeps his book of magic

A under a tree   **B** in his cave   **C** on the beach

4 Ferdinand has to

A cut wood for Prospero   **B** make a fire for Prospero   **C** bring wood to Prospero's cave

5 Prospero listens to Ferdinand and Miranda from

A behind a tree   **B** inside his cave   **C** the top of a hill

6 When Ariel brings food and drink to Alonso and his friends, he's dressed as a

A cook   **B** waiter   **C** farmer

7 Ariel then becomes a

A snake   **B** rat   **C** bird

8 When Stephano arrives in front of Prospero's cave, he finds

A the book of magic   **B** Ferdinand and Miranda   **C** clothes

9 The last thing Prospero asks Ariel to do is to

A wake up the captain and sailors   **B** prepare the ship   **C** take them home

10 At the end of the play Prospero

A decides to stay on the island   **B** throws away his book of magic   **C** goes away with Ariel

Syllabus

///

Level A2

This reader contains the items listed below as well as those included in previous levels of the ELI Readers syllabus

Verb tenses, forms and patterns

Present Simple   Present Continuous
Past Simple   Past Continuous
Present Perfect Simple with for, since, already, yet
Future with will
Affirmative, interrogative, negative forms of tenses
Imperatives
Passive forms: present simple and past simple
Verbs plus gerund, base form or infinitive (like, would like, want)

Modal verbs

Can, could
Must, have to, need
Should: advice

Types of clause

Main clause
Coordinate clause
Subordinate clause following sure, think, know, if, where, when, because
Defining relative clauses with who, where

Teen (ELI) Readers

Stage 1
Maureen Simpson, *In Search of a Missing Friend*
Charles Dickens, *Oliver Twist*
Geoffrey Chaucer, *Canterbury Tales*
J. Borsbey & R. Swan, *The Boat Race Mystery*
Lucy Maud Montgomery, *Anne of Green Gables*
Mark Twain, *A Connecticut Yankee in King Arthur's Court*
Angela Tomkinson, *Great Friends!*
Edith Nesbit, *The Railway Children*

Stage 2
Elizabeth Ferretti, *Dear Diary...*
Angela Tomkinson, *Loving London*
Mark Twain, *The Adventures of Tom Sawyer*
Mary Flagan, *The Egyptian Souvenir*
Maria Luisa Banfi, *A Faraway World*
Frances Hodgson Burnett, *The Secret Garden*
Robert Louis Stevenson, *Treasure Island*
Elizabeth Ferretti, *Adventure at Haydon Point*
William Shakespeare, *The Tempest*

Stage 3
Anna Claudia Ramos, *Expedition Brazil*
Charles Dickens, *David Copperfield*
Mary Flagan, *Val's Diary*
Maureen Simpson, *Destination Karminia*
Anonymous, *Robin Hood*
Jack London, *The Call of the Wild*
Louisa May Alcott, *Little Women*